Chilling Tales from Long Ago

Peter Hepplewhite &
Neil Tonge

Macdonald Young Books

CONTENTS

• • • • • □ Introduction 5

• • • • • □ The Curse of Tutankhamun 6

• • • • • □ Sitting Bull's Vision 11

• • • • • □ Beware the Ides of March! 16

• • • • • □ The Cursed Car of Sarajevo 20

• • • • • □ The Impossible Flight 25

• • • • • □ Glossary 30

• • • • • □ Index 31

INTRODUCTION

Do you believe in ghosts, spirits or people with special psychic powers? This book looks at how curious happenings connected with key historical events and personalities may have changed the course of history – forever.

Stories of the supernatural raise lots of questions. The five stories you are about to read are no exception – they ask some spine-chilling questions about the past:

Did the British archaeologists who discovered the tomb of the young Egyptian pharaoh Tutankhamun unleash an ancient curse that destroyed many innocent people?

Was Chief Sitting Bull's eerie vision of victory enough to save his people from the invasions of the 'white men'?

Did Julius Caesar die a violent death because he ignored warnings from the gods, or was it all just a terrible coincidence?

The car in which Archduke Ferdinand and his wife were assassinated brought bad luck and even death to later owners – but can objects really be cursed by tragic events?

RAF pilot Bill Corfield narrowly escaped death in 1947 when he made an 'impossible' flight – but what was the strange presence that stopped him from crashing?

Before you make up your mind about these stories, weigh up the evidence in the History Fact Files and check out the original photographs that provide the facts behind the fiction.

Only when you have studied all the evidence and decided for yourself will this history rest in peace!

THE CURSE OF TUTANKHAMUN

The Valley of the Kings was used as the burial ground of the kings and queens of Egypt from about 1573 BC to 1090 BC. Before this time the royal tombs had been built inside vast pyramids, most of which still stand near Cairo.

The Valley of the Kings marked the beginning of the journey to the afterlife for many pharaohs in Ancient Egypt.

THE VALLEY OF THE KINGS

Tutankhamun was a pharaoh, or king, of Ancient Egypt who lived over 3,000 years ago. He died when he was only eighteen years old, and his tomb lay undiscovered until the early twentieth century.

Many Ancient Egyptian pharaohs were buried in tombs in the Valley of the Kings. This valley lies between steep cliffs on the west bank of the River Nile in Egypt. It is a desolate place, with no trees or greenery to give protection from the burning sun. Ancient Egyptians buried treasures with their pharaohs, believing that these treasures would accompany the pharaohs to the afterlife. Although the tombs were carefully guarded and their entrances disguised, robbers often broke in and stole the treasures, risking terrible punishments if they were caught. But the tomb of Tutankhamun was so well concealed that no robber had ever reached the inner chambers.

A PATH TO THE AFTERLIFE?

On a bright November morning in 1922, the archaeologist Howard Carter woke up with a start. He looked at his watch and leapt out of bed. He had overslept. Why hadn't his servant woken him up at six o'clock as he did every morning? Where *was* his servant?

Suddenly the flap of the tent was pulled aside and Carter's servant rushed in, his robe covered in mud. 'Come quickly, sir! We've found something.'

Carter dressed hurriedly and ran towards the excavation site. Brushing people aside, he reached the edge of the site and stopped. On the floor below him, he could just see the outline of a stone step.

THE EXCAVATION

After several days of careful work, a flight of sixteen steps was revealed with a sealed plaster wall at the bottom. Carter gave instructions for the excavation to be covered until his friend Lord Carnarvon could join him and share in the excitement of breaking into this unknown tomb.

On 24 November Carter and Carnarvon stood together in front of the plaster wall. Could they at last be on the threshold of the tomb of Tutankhamun? They had been hoping for this moment for many years. Carter picked up his hammer and chisel. The wall rang with hammer blows and a piece of plaster broke away.

The moment of truth. Carter and Carnarvon about to knock through the plaster wall in November 1922.

HISTORY FACT FILE

The first king to choose a burial site in the Valley of the Kings was Tuthmosis I. He was buried in the middle of the night, in a tomb dug out of solid rock. But in spite of all the care, the tomb was robbed. The kings who ruled after Tuthmosis were buried nearby. Some tombs were robbed but others remained undisturbed for 3,000 years.

Hot dry air streamed out of the dark hole. Carter started to widen the opening. Carnarvon lit a candle and passed it to Carter. The candlelight revealed a tunnel filled with rubble.

It took two days to clear a passage through the tunnel to a second door. Again an opening was made and Carter held up a candle. As his eyes adjusted to the gloom, Carter began to see the outlines of various objects emerging from the darkness. Gold and jewels glinted as the candlelight fell on them. Carter knew these must be the pharaoh's treasures, waiting to accompany him to the afterlife.

'Can you see anything?' asked Lord Carnarvon anxiously.

'Oh yes, *wonderful* things,' answered Carter, his eyes now dazzled by the treasures.

Archaeologists began to explore the Valley of the Kings in the 1890s. In 1902 the American archaeologist Theodore Davis discovered the coffin and mummified body of King Akhenaten. Among the king's belongings, Davis found an inscription containing the name of Tutankhamun. He searched throughout the valley for the tomb of this famous pharaoh but found nothing.

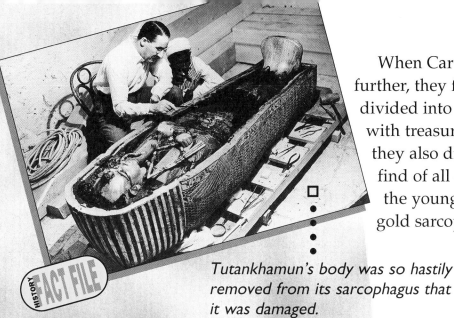

When Carter and Carnarvon probed further, they found that the tomb was divided into four chambers, each filled with treasures. And in the fourth chamber they also discovered the most amazing find of all – the mummified body of the young Tutankhamun in its gold sarcophagus.

Tutankhamun's body was so hastily removed from its sarcophagus that it was damaged.

Howard Carter and his wealthy patron Lord Carnarvon took up the search for Tutankhamun's tomb. Carter was convinced that it lay somewhere in the valley. He searched for ten years but found nothing. By 1922 Lord Carnarvon was growing impatient. So Carter returned to Egypt for a final search for the tomb of Tutankhamun.

A jewel from Tutankhamun's tomb. The winged scarab beetle was a symbol of life after death to the Ancient Egyptians.

Tutankhamun's magnificent gold burial mask.

THE CURSE OF THE KINGS

There are many tales of the curse connected to the tomb of Tutankhamun. One of the strangest involved a famous clairvoyant called Count Louis Hamon. He claimed to have seen the ghost of Tutankhamun's sister, who had warned him of the dangers of breaking into her brother's tomb. Count Hamon wrote to Lord Carnarvon, because he knew that Carnarvon was searching for Tutankhamun's tomb in the Valley of the Kings.

'I now know the Ancient Egyptians had knowledge and power of which today we have no comprehension. In the name of God, I beg you to take care,' Hamon warned.

The letter arrived too late. Carter and Carnarvon had already broken through the seals into the tomb, ignoring the warning above the entrance.

Lord Carnarvon was so absorbed in the discovery of the treasures that he took little notice of a mosquito bite which had appeared on his cheek. But the bite became infected and he died within forty-seven days of the opening of the tomb. It is said that Tutankhamun's mummified face had a scar in exactly the same place as Carnarvon's mosquito bite.

Lord Carnarvon's death and the strange tales surrounding it reminded people of an ancient legend about the 'curse of the kings'. This story would almost certainly have been told at the time of the young king's burial to frighten off tomb robbers.

But there were more deaths of people connected with the opening of the tomb. Ali Farmy Bey, an Egyptian prince who had visited the tomb shortly after its discovery, was murdered in a London hotel and his brother committed suicide. Lord Westbury's son, who had helped Carter on the dig, died suddenly and mysteriously. A few days before he himself died, Lord Westbury is supposed to have said, 'I can't stand any more horrors.'

In the end, an astounding twenty-one deaths were blamed on the curse of Tutankhamun's tomb.

The well-known clairvoyant Count Hamon claimed he had received a warning from the ghost of Tutankhamun's sister.

HISTORY FACT FILE

Howard Carter died of natural causes in 1939. Investigations also revealed that neither Lord Westbury's death nor that of his son had any connection with Tutankhamun's tomb.

SITTING BULL'S VISION

A GREAT INDIAN CHIEF

In 1876 Sitting Bull was the chief of the Hunkpapa – one of the tribes of Sioux Indians on the Great Plains in North America. He was forty-six years old and by now he was familiar with the ways of the white men. He knew he couldn't trust them. In 1868 the Treaty of Laramie had declared that the Powder River Country was Indian territory. But gold miners were pouring into the region to hack at the Black Hills and the United States army had been sent to protect them. The Black Hills were sacred to the Sioux so they had to fight to defend their land.

The Sioux tribes respected Chief Sitting Bull. Tales of his great bravery were often told around camp fires. A favourite tale was the story of the 'first coup'. Young Slow (as Sitting Bull was then called) was only fourteen when he joined a raiding party to steal horses from the Crows, traditional enemies of the Sioux. He proudly painted on his war colours – his body yellow and his pony bright red.

HISTORY FACT FILE

In the early seventeenth century, Europeans landed on the east coast of North America and founded settlements. Soon the first wars against the native Americans, or Indians as they were called, took place. In most cases, the Indians' weapons were no match for the guns of the 'white men'.

• • • □

If a Sioux warrior struck an enemy with his coup stick and then escaped unharmed, he had proved his skill and bravery to the tribe.

By 1830 many of the great eastern tribes of Indians such as the Iroquois, Ottowa, Shawnee and Cherokee had been broken up and driven from their lands. Some of these tribespeople went to the Great Plains of North America, the last stronghold of free native Americans.

Deadwood, Dakota. Miners carved out towns like this in the sacred Black Hills of the Sioux.

When battle came, Slow charged ahead. Seeing him closing in, one of the Crows took aim with a bow and arrow. Slow dodged the arrow, fearlessly struck the Crow with his coup stick and galloped away. After this exploit, Slow's proud father gave him a very powerful name – *Ta-tan-ka I-yo-ta-ke*, or Sitting Bull.

SITTING BULL'S RED BLANKET

As the US army prepared to attack the Plains Indians in the summer of 1876, Sitting Bull called the tribes together, not only the Sioux but also old enemies like the Cheyenne and the Arapaho. He had a blunt message for them all.

'We must stand together or the soldiers will wipe us out, one by one. They want war. We will give it to them,' Sitting Bull said.

A great army of Plains Indians slowly assembled – 4,000 warriors and their families. But even as they made their plans, Sitting Bull knew the US soldiers were closing in. How could the Indians win this important battle? Sitting Bull asked Wakan Tanka, the Great Spirit, for help. Wakan Tanka told Sitting Bull that he should call up the power of the spirit world by carrying out a sun dance. During the dance, Sitting Bull should make a sacrifice – a 'red blanket' of his own blood.

The preparations for the sacred ceremony were made. The bravest warriors were sent to cut down a tree. The tree was set upright in the camp and became the centre of the dance. In the dawn of 14 June 1876, Sitting Bull began the ceremony. He knew his suffering would be terrible, but to cry out in pain would be a disgrace. He sat down with his back against the tree and began to pray, wailing the singsong words into the air above the hushed crowds.

Sitting Bull had chosen a young brave called Jumping Bull to perform the sacrifice. Jumping Bull was strong and his hand was steady. He thrust the pointed tip of a steel awl into Sitting Bull's right wrist. The point flicked into the flesh and lifted a small piece of skin. Jumping Bull skilfully sliced the skin off with his knife. He repeated this a hundred times across Sitting Bull's arms.

Throughout his ordeal Sitting Bull sat up straight, without flinching, and continued his prayer. By the end of the ritual, the blood was flowing down his arms and dripping off his fingertips. This was Sitting Bull's red blanket.

 After the American Civil War of 1861–65, growing numbers of white settlers began to cross the Great Plains, heading for the fertile lands of the west coast. The Sioux were the largest Plains Indian tribe and they fought the settlers. In 1868 Chief Red Cloud forced the US government to sign the Treaty of Laramie, which stated that the Powder River Country as far as the Bighorn mountains 'shall be considered Indian territory'.

13

"Sioux Indian Council" painted in 1847 by George Catlin, a white artist who visited Indian tribes to record their customs.

THE POWER OF THE SUN DANCE

But the time of suffering for Sitting Bull was not yet over. Rising to his feet, he began to dance around the tree. All through the long, hot day he danced to the rhythm of his prayer. Without food or water he danced till the sun set, and then on through the night. By dawn Sitting Bull was exhausted. But he danced until noon and then collapsed.

As Sitting Bull lay on the ground the vision came to him. The mist in front of his eyes cleared and he could see US soldiers falling from the skies like grasshoppers. The soldiers tumbled into the Sioux camp, their heads bent and their hats in the dust. They were beaten men.

When Sitting Bull had recovered, he told the Sioux tribes they would win a great victory. But he also gave them a warning: 'These soldiers are gifts of Wakan Tanka. Kill them but do not take their guns or horses. If you set your hearts on the goods of the white men, you will bring a curse on this nation.'

THE BATTLE OF LITTLE BIGHORN

On 25 June 1876 General Custer surveyed the Sioux camp through his field glasses. He was sure all the braves were out hunting, so he led the 7th Cavalry in an attack against the women and children. But the Sioux warriors were waiting. Led by Crazy Horse, the warriors slaughtered General Custer and his 215 men at the Battle of Little Bighorn. Wild with excitement, the Sioux warriors looted the dead soldiers, carrying off rifles, horses and uniforms. Sitting Bull's vision had come true, but he took no pleasure in it. Wakan Tanka's warning had been ignored.

HISTORY FACT FILE

In 1876 the US government broke the Treaty of Laramie and sent in troops to protect the US miners' search for gold in the Black Hills. Sitting Bull raised a great army of Plains Indians and used his vision to prepare his people for battle. His courage fired the fighting spirit of the warriors and convinced them that victory was certain. Crazy Horse led the Indian attack and wiped out General Custer's 7th Cavalry at the Battle of Little Bighorn.

This is from Otto Becker's painting "Custer's Last Stand at the Battle of Little Bighorn, 25 June 1876". Custer did not find the easy victory that he had expected.

The Battle of Little Bighorn was a huge victory but it was short-lived. The American people demanded revenge for the deaths of Custer and his troops, and US soldiers swarmed over the Powder River Country. The Indians were quickly defeated and their lands stolen. In 1890 Sitting Bull was shot by Indian police working for the white men. Sadly he had lived long enough to see both parts of his vision come true.

BEWARE THE IDES OF MARCH!

CAESAR'S PROBLEM

On a January morning in 44 BC Julius Caesar, ruler of the great Roman Empire and the most feared man in ancient Rome, was jolted awake. Memories of a terrible nightmare came flooding into his mind. He had been swooping through the air at terrifying speed towards Mount Olympus, the home of the gods. Jupiter, the chief of the gods, had taken his hand and led him away. Looking back at the Earth, Caesar had cried out, 'Not yet, not yet.'

HISTORY FACT FILE

From 500 BC to AD 500, the city of Rome ruled one of the greatest empires of the ancient world. In 60 BC Caesar became one of three rulers of Rome – the others were Crassus and Pompey. Caesar soon showed that he could be a ruthless ruler. Between 58 BC and 50 BC, Caesar's armies conquered the Celtic tribes living in the countries now called France, Switzerland and Belgium, and added their lands to the Roman Empire.

Julius Caesar was middle-aged now and his health and strength were beginning to fail. He had slept badly for weeks and his dreams were frightening. Caesar was planning a huge attack on the Parthian Empire (modern-day Iran) in the Middle East. A great force of sixteen legions (about 80,000 men) and 10,000 cavalry had been gathered in readiness for the attack. If Caesar could conquer the Parthians he could claim to be the finest general since Alexander the Great, who had won a mighty empire three centuries earlier.

Would Caesar's plans be successful? Time was pressing and Caesar knew that his enemies, fearful of his power, were plotting his downfall. He desperately needed to know what the future held in store for him. Caesar realized that one man could help him – Spurinna the soothsayer. With his mystic powers Spurinna could read the omens, or signs, of events to come.

SPURINNA'S WARNING

With his bodyguard struggling to keep up with him, Caesar marched briskly to Spurinna's temple. This was the Temple of Jupiter, the grandest in Rome. As he stepped out of the icy winter wind into the shadows of the temple, Caesar came face to face with Spurinna.

'I have important decisions to make. I need to know the way of things,' Caesar said bluntly, not wanting to reveal his plans.

Spurinna nodded and led Caesar into the darkness of a private shrine. He ordered an animal to be brought in to be sacrificed so that he could answer Caesar's question. As it was a big question and therefore needed a big sacrifice, Caesar's servants brought in a bull.

Silently they watched the bull being slaughtered. Spurinna gazed into the animal's entrails. He traced the shape of the liver with his fingers. The expression on his face was grim.

'You are in grave danger,' Spurinna told Caesar. 'This danger will not pass until after the Ides of March (15 March). Until then you must be patient and avoid all risks.'

Caesar also landed briefly in Britain, although the conquest of Britain took place after his death.

This stone sculpture decorated the Temple of Neptune in ancient Rome. It shows a bull being brought to the soothsayer for sacrifice. Romans believed they could learn about the future by examining an animal's internal organs. • • •

17

Caesar was a brilliant general who shared the dangers of battle with his troops. In 49 BC, after the death of Crassus, Caesar declared war on Rome itself. His enemies were led by Pompey, also a great general. The fighting spirit of Caesar's armies brought him victory and Pompey fled. By 45 BC, Caesar controlled the whole Roman Empire and members of the Senate feared his power.

Caesar considered Spurinna's warning and decided to ignore it. He had ignored bad omens in the past. He remembered the time he had arrived in Africa. He had slipped and fallen as he stepped on to African soil for the first time. The troops watching him had been shocked. This was a bad omen before an approaching battle. But thinking quickly, Caesar had thrown out his arms and hugged the ground, shouting, 'Africa, I have tight hold of you.' At once the men had cheered up and they went on to win the battle. Caesar had made his own fate then and he would do so again.

A PLOT TO MURDER

In the weeks following Caesar's visit to Spurinna, his plans to attack the Parthian Empire went ahead. Men who were loyal to him were given important posts in Rome and everything seemed safe. Caesar would leave with his troops by 18 March at the latest.

Caesar's enemies were in despair. For 450 years Rome had been a republic, ruled by elected senators. Now Caesar had made himself dictator for life. It seemed that all the things the Romans valued, such as freedom, honour and ancient rights, were being trampled on. What would Caesar do next – make himself king?

A group of senators secretly began to plot Caesar's murder. The senators knew that to get past his bodyguards, they would have to attack Caesar in an open space. Caesar solved their problem by calling a meeting of the Senate in the Pompeian Assembly Room. This large hall would make a perfect killing ground. The date he had chosen for the meeting was 15 March – the Ides of March!

THE FATEFUL DAY

On the morning of 15 March, Caesar strode confidently from his house. One panic-stricken plotter tried to warn the dictator and thrust a note containing details of the attack into his hands. But Caesar tucked the note into a pile of documents he was carrying, without looking at it.

As he arrived at the hall, Caesar saw Spurinna. 'Look,' he cried, 'the Ides of March have come and I am safe.'

'Aye,' replied Spurinna, 'they have come. But they have not gone yet.'

When Caesar sat down, the senators struck. One of them fell on his knees in front of Caesar and grabbed his robe. This was the signal for the others to move in. Knife after knife flashed down, cruelly stabbing, until the great ruler collapsed and died.

Looking on, Spurinna felt little pity. Caesar had been warned. Those who ignored the omens did so at their peril.

This painting by Vincenzo Camuccini, 1773–1844, shows Caesar being stabbed to death on the Ides of March, 44 BC.

19

THE CURSED CAR OF SARAJEVO

In 1914, six great European powers were grouped together in two strong alliances. Britain, France and Russia formed the Triple Entente, while Germany, Austria-Hungary and Italy formed the Triple Alliance. Each power agreed to help the other powers in its alliance if any one of them was attacked.

Archduke Franz Ferdinand and his wife in Sarajevo on the morning of 28 June 1914.

A DANGEROUS PLACE

Several places in Europe could have caused a flashpoint for the outbreak of the First World War in 1914. But nowhere was more dangerous at that time than the Balkan peninsula in south-east Europe. In 1908 the huge Austro-Hungarian army had marched into Bosnia-Herzegovina, seizing the country from Turkish rule. This takeover was resented by many people living in the Balkans, especially the Serbs.

Emperor Franz Josef, ruler of the vast Austro-Hungarian Empire, decided to send his heir, Archduke Franz Ferdinand, on a visit to Bosnia. He hoped that a royal visit would make the people of this part of his empire loyal to him.

The royal train steamed into the station at Sarajevo, the capital of Bosnia, on the morning of 28 June 1914. On board were the archduke and his wife, on the first stage of the journey that was to lead to disaster for the whole of Europe.

THE ROYAL VISIT

The day was already hot. All over Europe people were enjoying a long heatwave that showed no signs of ending. Bands played and crowds cheered as Archduke Franz Ferdinand and Countess Sophie stepped out of the train. But not everyone in the crowd was celebrating.

A secret Serbian organization called the 'Black Hand' was plotting murder, and Gavrillo Princip, one of its members, lay in wait for the royal couple.

The Austrian police knew about a plot against Franz Ferdinand and his wife but they took no extra precautions to protect them.

Countess Sophie had dreamt that she and her husband were lying in a pool of blood. She had told the archduke about her dream but he took no notice and ignored all security measures.

'We are in God's hands,' Franz Ferdinand told officials.

The archduke and the countess climbed into a red open-topped car, which allowed them to be seen easily by the people. Only 120 policemen lined the route, helped by a few detectives mingling with the crowds. During the ride to the civic hall, a bomb was thrown at the car. It missed and no one was hurt. The archduke turned to the Chief of Police.

'What about these bombs? Will it happen again?' Franz Ferdinand asked.

'Your Imperial Highness, you can travel quite happily. I take full responsibility,' was the firm reply.

HISTORY FACT FILE

At this time most people thought that such strong alliances between countries would help to keep the peace. They did not believe that any country would risk a war in which there would be enormous destruction. It was felt that even the winners in such a war would suffer huge loss of life and the destruction of industries.

THE FATAL MISTAKE

After the reception at the civic hall, a new return route to the station was planned. Unfortunately, no one told the driver. When it was realized that the car was returning on the original route, the Chief of Police shouted angrily to the driver, 'What's this? Stop! You're going the wrong way.'

By a terrible coincidence, the driver braked close to a crowded pavement where Gavrillo Princip was standing. With his victims delivered straight into his hands, Princip did not hesitate. Reaching inside his jacket, he took out his gun and leapt on to the running-board of the car. He took aim and laughed as he shot the royal couple at point-blank range. The countess died first. A bullet had penetrated her throat and she choked to death. The archduke died a few seconds later. A bullet had pierced the right side of his coat collar, cut through his throat and lodged in his spine.

The murders on that hot June day in 1914 set in motion the course of events that led to war.

Princip was arrested immediately after the assassination. He was too young for the death penalty and died in an Austrian prison in April 1918.

HISTORY FACT FILE

The deaths of Archduke Franz Ferdinand and his wife were the spark that set off war throughout Europe. Austria-Hungary blamed the Serbs for the murders, declared war on Serbia and asked Germany for help. Russia believed itself to be the protector of Serbia and so declared war on Austria. Russia then called on its alliance with France. Britain supported her allies, Russia and France. When war broke out, Italy remained neutral and then joined the alliance with Britain, France and Russia in 1915.

A GRUESOME REPUTATION

What happened to the car that had carried the Archduke and his wife to their deaths? This vehicle soon began to earn a sinister reputation, as if some powerful and unknown force was attracting further disasters.

After the end of the First World War the car was repaired and sold. Soon the car's new owner was involved in a dreadful accident and his right arm was torn off. He had several more accidents in the car and decided to have the vehicle destroyed. However, a friend, Dr Srikis, begged him not to destroy the car but to give it to him.

The First World War was the most terrible war ever fought up to this time. It dragged on for over four years. More than ten million men were killed, and many more were disabled.

All went well for a while and the car seemed to be losing its bad reputation. But then Dr Srikis was found dead, crushed beneath the upturned car on a lonely road.

Another doctor acquired the car. But when he learnt of its sinister history, he swore he could see bloodstains on the back seat. He sold the car to a racing driver. In a race through the mountains, the car left the road and hit a wall. The driver's neck was broken.

The car's last private owner was a man called Tiber Hirshfield. He had the car repainted in a pleasant blue colour, hoping that this would bring about a change in its fortunes. The car's first outing in its new colour was to a wedding. Hirshfield took five friends with him. The car was involved in a collision and all six were killed.

A museum seemed the best place to put a car of such historic interest, so it was bought by a museum in Vienna, the capital of Austria. The curator, Karl Brunner, knew about the car's reputation. He forbade anyone to sit in the car so as not to tempt fate. He feared there might be more deaths or accidents.

And finally? Well, the story is not quite complete. During the Second World War, the museum was bombed and much of it was destroyed. Karl Brunner was in the museum at the time of the raid but his body was never found. The car, however, survived...

The car that never lost its reputation for bringing bad luck can still be seen today in a museum in Vienna.

24

THE CORFIELD BROTHERS

Jimmy Corfield was a bomber pilot in the British Royal Air Force (RAF) during the Second World War, which broke out between Germany, and Britain and France in September 1939. Jimmy's younger brother Bill wanted to follow in Jimmy's footsteps. When Jimmy came home on leave in July 1941, Bill told him that he was going to join the RAF as a pilot.

'Don't bother, you haven't got the temperament for it. Get a job as ground crew,' Jimmy replied.

Bill worshipped his older brother and he was shocked and hurt by these remarks.

On 12 August 1941 Jimmy Corfield was taking part in a daylight raid by Blenheim bombers on factories near the German city of Cologne. The raid was extremely dangerous because the Blenheim was a small, slow plane and in broad daylight it was at the mercy of German fighter planes and anti-aircraft guns. Jimmy survived the raid but his plane was hit by anti-aircraft guns on his way back to Britain and he crashed into the North Sea.

The Second World War began in September 1939. Britain and France declared war on Germany after German troops invaded Poland. By the spring of 1942, German armies occupied most of Europe.

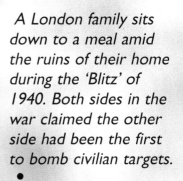

A London family sits down to a meal amid the ruins of their home during the 'Blitz' of 1940. Both sides in the war claimed the other side had been the first to bomb civilian targets.

During 1940–41 German bombers 'blitzed' London and other British cities. In June 1941 German armies invaded Russia. British planes were ordered to bomb German factories to take some of the pressure off the Russian troops, who were desperately trying to defend their homeland.

Jimmy's body was washed up on the coast of Holland two weeks later. When the tragic news reached home, Bill understood why his brother had made his earlier unkind remarks. Jimmy had known how dangerous it was to be a bomber pilot and he had been trying to save his brother's life. But Bill was not put off. He joined the RAF and became a pilot. After the war ended, he remained in the RAF.

A FEROCIOUS STORM

It was January 1947. The storm broke with fury around the tiny Anson aircraft. Torrents of rain hammered against the thin fabric of the plane. The crash of thunder bellowed over the drone of the twin engines. Forked lightning flashed out of the black clouds, briefly illuminating the dark waters of the Mediterranean Sea below. The pilot, Bill Corfield, cursed and mumbled quietly to himself, 'How on earth did the weather forecasters miss this? Surely the radar should have picked it up?'

As the strength of the storm grew, the flimsy plane was buffeted around the sky.

'We can't take much more of this,' Bill said to his navigator and radio operator, 'I'm taking her as low as I can before we're torn apart.'

Steering through the raging winds, Bill took the Anson down until the plane was skimming barely fifteen metres above the crests of the waves. Here the winds were a little easier but visibility was almost gone. The crew had no way of spotting the chain of islands that marked their path to Athens.

Bill glanced at the fuel gauge with a sense of dread. Fuel was always critical on a long flight, but with the extra amount needed by the engines to beat the storm, there was little in reserve. If they did not find the Greek coast soon they would have to ditch in the sea. Bill hoped he could land on the waves without breaking up the Anson, but in these conditions they had a very poor chance of surviving such a landing.

BILL'S DECISION

Suddenly there was a shout from the navigator: 'There's the coastline ahead. It should be the Greek mainland.'

With a sigh of relief, Bill began looking for a beach on which to make an emergency landing. He searched the shore frantically but all he could see were barren rocks. His hopes of survival began to fade.

When the Second World War ended in 1945, the RAF still had a huge job to do. Britain was slowly giving independence to a great empire, including modern-day India, Pakistan and Bangladesh. The RAF flew in troops and equipment to many small wars and emergencies. Bill Corfield and his Anson were on their way to Singapore, a key port in the Far East, when they were caught in the storm near Greece.

The Avro Anson was the workhorse of the RAF from 1933 to 1956. The Anson was so reliable that pilots nicknamed the plane 'faithful Annie'.

'Corinth Canal coming up ahead,' the navigator said, grimly pleased that at last he knew exactly where they were. And without thinking, Bill took the strangest action of his life. He swung the Anson into the shelter of the high, narrow walls of the great ship canal.

At once the shrieking wind vanished – it was like flying through the peace and calm of a cathedral. But Bill wasn't calm. He realized that if he made one small slip the plane would smash against the sheer rock sides of the narrow canal. What had he done? His hands were sticky with sweat. His breath came in short gasps. He couldn't do this. He needed help before they were all killed.

'Jimmy wouldn't have been so stupid,' Bill muttered to himself. 'Jimmy would have known what to do.'

JIMMY TAKES OVER

Suddenly a deep sense of peace came over Bill. He knew help had arrived and he wasn't flying the plane alone. Jimmy was there. Not standing beside him but inside his head. Strong, capable Jimmy, the big brother he loved. Jimmy the bomber pilot, who had been shot down and had drowned in 1941.

Bill relaxed in his seat and Jimmy took over, working Bill's hands on the steering column. The Anson skimmed between the walls of the canal without wavering – its compass needle seeming frozen as the plane flew dead straight.

At the end of the canal they soared out over a calmer sea. Bill did not wait for instructions from the navigator. Jimmy knew the way. The plane headed towards the safety of Athens airport and in a few minutes the lights of the city shone through the darkness. The Anson made a perfect landing and began to taxi towards the control tower. As it trundled along the ground the engine spluttered and died. The fuel had run out. Jimmy had got them through just in time.

The next day Bill wrote up his flight report. He did not mention Jimmy but reported the life-saving dash through the Corinth Canal. He was laughed at. Were these crazy Englishmen making up stories to hide where they had really flown? The Greek authorities knew that the canal was only just wider than the wing tips of the Anson. Bill's flight was clearly impossible...

The Corinth Canal in Greece is 5.5 km long. Built in 1893, the canal links the Aegean Sea to the Gulf of Corinth and the Ionian Sea.

GLOSSARY

☐ **Afterlife** The 'place' where the spirit of an Egyptian was believed to go after death.

☐ **Alliance** An agreement between people or nations to work together.

☐ **Awl** A sharp, pointed tool for piercing holes.

☐ **Balkans** The countries of the Balkan peninsula – Slovenia, Croatia, Bosnia, Serbia, Montenegro, Macedonia, Albania, Bulgaria, Turkey and Greece.

☐ **Brave** A native North American tribal warrior.

☐ **Clairvoyant** Someone who has the power to perceive things that will happen in the future.

☐ **Curator** The person in charge of a museum.

☐ **Dictator** An all-powerful ruler.

☐ **Entrails** The insides of an animal's body – its intestines.

☐ **Excavate** To dig up something from below ground.

☐ **Ides** The fifteenth day of March, May, July and October in the Roman calendar.

☐ **Legions** Military units of the Roman army.

☐ **Mummify** To embalm and preserve a body for burial.

☐ **Patron** Someone who supports and helps to pay for a project.

☐ **Psychic** Relating to powers outside the range of normal experience.

☐ **Radar** A radio device used to locate the position of ships, aircraft, or other objects (usually moving) in darkness or fog. Radar can also detect certain types of storm.

☐ **Republic** A state or nation that has a form of government without a king or queen.

☐ **Ritual** A set way of performing a ceremony, usually sacred or religious.

☐ **Running-board** A footboard along the side of early motor cars.

☐ **Sacrifice** An offering to the gods.

☐ **Sarcophagus** A stone, lead, wooden or terracotta coffin, often highly decorated.

☐ **Senator** A member of the government of ancient Rome.

☐ **Shrine** A place of worship.

☐ **Sioux** The largest of the North American Plains Indian tribes. (The Hunkpapa were a branch of the Lakota Sioux.)

☐ **Soothsayer** Someone who claims to be able to read the future.

☐ **Supernatural** Relating to something that cannot be explained by natural laws.

☐ **Treaty** A contract between two or more countries.

FURTHER READING

The Encyclopedia of Ghosts and Spirits by John and Anne Spencer (Headline, 1992)
Mysterious World: The Supernatural by Ivor Baddiel and Tracey Blezard (Macdonald Young Books, 1998)
The Paranormal: An Illustrated Encyclopedia by Stuart Gordon (Headline, 1992)
The Unexplained: Hauntings by Peter Hepplewhite and Neil Tonge (Hamlyn, 1997)

INDEX

● ● □ alliances, First World War 20, 21, 22
American Civil War 13
Anson aircraft 26, 27, 28, 29
archaeologists 6, 8

● ● □ Battle of Little Bighorn 15
'Black Hand' 21
Black Hills 11, 12, 15
'Blitz' 25
Brunner, Karl 24

● ● □ Caesar, Julius 5, 16–19
car of Sarajevo, curse of 5, 23–24
Carnarvon, Lord 7, 8, 9, 10
Carter, Howard 6, 7, 8, 9, 10
Corfield, Bill 5, 25–29
Corfield, Jimmy 25, 26, 28, 29
Corinth Canal 28, 29
Crazy Horse 15
Crows 11, 12
curse of Tutankhamun 5, 9–10
Custer, General 15

● ● □ excavation (Tutankhamun's tomb) 7

● ● □ First World War 20, 22, 23
flight, Bill Corfield's 5, 26–29
Franz Ferdinand, Archduke 5, 20, 21, 22
Franz Josef, Emperor 20

● ● □ Hamon, Count Louis 9, 10
Hirshfield, Tiber 24

● ● □ Ides of March 17, 18, 19

● ● □ Parthian Empire 16, 18
Pearl Harbor 26
pharaohs (kings) 6, 7, 8
pilots, bomber 25, 26, 29
Plains Indians 12, 13
Powder River Country 11, 13, 15
Princip, Gavrillo 21, 22

● ● □ raids, bombing 25, 26
red blanket, Sitting Bull's 12, 13
Roman Empire 16, 18
Royal Air Force (RAF) 25, 26, 27

● ● □ Second World War 24, 25, 26, 27
senators, Roman 18, 19
Sioux Indians 11, 12, 13, 14, 15
Sitting Bull, Chief 5, 11–15
Sophie, Countess 20, 21, 22
Spurinna the soothsayer 17, 18, 19
Srikis, Dr 23, 24
sun dance 12, 14

● ● □ tombs 6, 7, 8, 9, 10
treasures 6, 8, 9
Treaty of Laramie 11, 13, 15
Tutankhamun 5, 6, 7, 9, 10

● ● □ Valley of the Kings 6, 7, 8, 9
vision, Sitting Bull's 5, 14, 15

● ● □ Wakan Tanka 12, 14, 15